BEAUTIFUL BROWN SKIN CHILD

AN ODE TO OUR CHILDREN

By Ayesha Rodriguez

This book is for: _____

From:_____

Library of Congress Cataloging-in-Publication Data
ISBN: 978-1-7356650-3-0

Publisher Jaye Squared Youth Empowerment Services, INC.
Website: www.ayesharodriguez.com

Illustration copyright © 2020 by Rina Risnawati

Layout Design by Susan Gulash
Gulash Graphics, Lutz, FL

Beautiful brown skin child, you are a sight to behold. Your melanin is so rich and you have a heart of gold.

Beautiful brown skin child you hail from Queens and Kings, though history does not always reveal these things.

Beautiful brown skin child, I love your smile.
Know who you are and keep your head held high.

I AM

special.
worthy.
kind.
smart.
important.
loved.
able.
thankful.
enough.

Beautiful brown skin child, I believe in you.
Keep the faith and courage in all you do.

Beautiful brown skin child, you make me so proud.
Love your blackness and say it out loud.

Beautiful brown skin child, you are more powerful than you know. Please always remember this as you grow.

Beautiful brown skin child, you are so intelligent.
Do not let anyone ever tell you different.

Beautiful brown skin child, there is a leader in you.
Put no limits on the great things that you can do.

Beautiful brown skin child, don't forget to fight.
Fight for your future and for what is right.

Beautiful brown skin child, it is okay to cry.
Life's journey has many lows and highs.

Beautiful brown skin child, don't you ever give up.
Get the help that you need to refill your cup.

Beautiful brown skin child, please focus and be wise. Be a seeker of truth and stay far from the lies.

Beautiful brown skin child, I love you so much. You are worthy of goodness and deserve to be treated as such!

Daily Activity:

Do you know what an affirmation is? An affirmation is a positive word or sentence that you repeat to yourself to help remind you of who you are. Stand in the mirror every day and repeat the affirmations on the next page. Say it proudly and loudly! I want you to really believe every affirmation, just like I do! If people say things to you that are not nice, you will know in your heart that it is not true. You are amazing and I'm so proud of you!

I am special.

I am worthy.

I am kind.

I am smart.

I am important.

I am loved.

I am able.

I am thankful.

I am enough.

I am glad to be me!

Discussion Questions

1. What is melanin?

2. What do you love about yourself? (When you respond, please start with, "I am")

3. It is important to talk about our feelings with someone that we trust. Who do you talk to when you are feeling sad?

4. You are so smart! What subjects do you like to learn about? Why is it important to study?

5. We make choices every day. What are some good choices that you have made? How did they make you feel?

6. In the book, why do you think they are walking and holding signs?

7. Can you think of healthy habits that you should do every day?

8. What makes someone a good leader?

9. To be mindful means that you are paying attention to your feelings. Some people like to practice mindfulness by sitting quietly, writing in a journal, taking deep breaths, drawing or coloring. What are some mindful activities that help you to be calm?

10. Why is it important to learn about your history?

About the Author

Ayesha Rodriguez is an author, speaker, educator and entrepreneur. Most importantly, she is the mom to two wonderful children. She is dedicated to creating books and products that positively reflect the diversity of children. She enjoys spending quality time with loved ones and traveling.

To learn more about her, please visit: www.ayesharodriguez.com

CPSIA information can be obtained
at www.ICGtesting.com
Printed in the USA
LVHW071606300322
714781LV00009B/416

9 781735 665030